MY CAT

St. Clare of Montefalco School

Written by Alice E. Lisson
Illustrated by Dara Goldman

My cat loves to nap.

I love to play.

My cat loves to nap.

4

I love to jump.

My cat loves to nap.

I love to ride.

My cat loves to play.

No, cat, no!

It's my time to nap!